Klaus Paysan

CREATURES
of Pond and Pool

Edited by Sylvia Johnson

Lerner Publications Company
Minneapolis, Minnesota

First published in the United States 1971 by Lerner Publications Company,
Minneapolis, Minnesota. All English language rights reserved.

Published simultaneously in Canada by J. M. Dent & Sons Ltd., Don Mills, Ontario.

Copyright © MCMLXVIII by Deutsche Verlags-Anstalt, Stuttgart, Germany.

Photographs and text by Klaus Paysan, sketches by Angela Paysan.
English translation by Jane Owen.

Standard Book Number: 8225-0562-2
Library of Congress Catalog Card Number: 77-102893

Printed in Germany and bound in the United States.

CONTENTS

EDITOR'S NOTE

An understanding of the scientific system of classification can be helpful in observing and reading about the creatures of ponds and pools. This system, part of a science called taxonomy, is an attempt to classify all living things into related groups on the basis of the likenesses and differences among them. *Species* is the basic unit of scientific classification. Creatures belonging to the same species have many common characteristics which set them apart from other living things. A *genus* is made up of two or more species; genus members are similar, but they differ in significant ways. The next largest group is family, then order, class, phylum, and finally, kingdom. By using this classification system, a scientist can study the animals native to his region in relation to living things throughout the world. The science of taxonomy makes use of an international language, Latin, so that all creatures may be given names which can be recognized by people everywhere. Each creature is usually identified by a two-part name. The European marsh frog, for ex-

ample, is *Rana ridibunda;* it belongs to the genus *Rana,* the species *ridibunda.*

Most of the amphibians, reptiles, and insects described in this book live in and around European ponds and pools. These creatures are similar to but not identical with American amphibians, reptiles, and insects. In some cases, a species native to Europe is also found in North America. More frequently, however, American and European creatures are members of the same genus but belong to different species. Sometimes the differences between European and American animals are great enough to necessitate their being classified in different genera (the Latin plural of genus). In the following pages, we have attempted to point out the relationships and similarities between the European and American creatures whenever possible. Despite the differences which do exist, all the animals described here belong to an international community of living things that depend on the environment of the freshwater pond for their existence.

INTRODUCTION

The most unforgettable events of my youth were not long holiday journeys to distant places but the frequent trips I made to the ponds and pools near my home town. My friends and I often came back from these trips covered with mud, and sometimes one of us would be punished for bringing home a frog wrapped in a handkerchief. But we were always drawn back to the magic world of the pond and the varied creatures that inhabited it. Here colorful newts gathered in the spring to lay their eggs on the water plants. Numerous common toads swam by, dragging their jellylike strings of black eggs through the water. Alpine toads stretched their round heads above the surface of the pond to seize the grasshoppers that we threw them. In the summer dragonflies darted across the water, their wide-spread wings shimmering in the sun.

I have never outgrown my childhood fascination with the creatures of ponds and pools. In all seasons and in any kind of weather I still visit the pond, even when crane flies and gadflies sting in the heavy calm before a thunderstorm. It is a great pleasure to see young frogs with stumpy tails, leaving the water in the hundreds and hopping madly over to the shade of the woods. There they catch their first meal on land and then look for a hiding hole which is damp enough for their sensitive skins. Reed-beds of ponds are fascinating in early summer. There is a dragonfly nymph creeping up every stem or resting motionless in one place; hours later the insect's shell will burst open to reveal a shining jewel. The experience of seeing this change is given only to a patient person. At first the hatching dragonfly is a pale creature with tiny, folded-up wings. Exhausted by the hard task of emerging from its shell, it hangs upside down from the reed blade. Then after a long rest it comes to life. The wings are pumped up and the observer can see them expanding. In the next pause the colors come and the soft wings harden. After an opalescent stage they become clear as crystal, streaked with black veins. The development of the wings is followed by a tense moment — the first flight. The first wing beats are clumsy but soon the natural rhythm is established and the dragonfly streaks through the air like a shimmering flash of lightning, stopping now and then to catch food or to fight for territory.

It is possible to spend hours on the banks of a pond, absorbed in watching dragonflies and other pond creatures. One can also observe pond life at home, but there are problems involved in such a venture. Parents, particularly mothers, often find it difficult to tolerate the menagerie of frogs and toads which an enthusiastic young person brings home in jars, boxes, plastic bags, and, if necessary, in his pockets. However, a little bit of organization can make life with pond creatures tolerable. First of all, suitable housing must be provided for the animals. Today one can buy simple terrariums, containers with glass or screen sides and tops, which can be made into satisfactory homes for amphibians and reptiles. Creatures that spend all their time in the water can be kept in an aquarium. All captive pond animals should be given adequate living space and proper food and care so that they may adapt successfully to their new surroundings.

After getting to know an individual animal thoroughly, one can return to the pond better prepared to study the behavior of similar creatures. Unfortunately, observation in such a natural setting is becoming increasingly difficult in our modern world. Many marshes, ponds, and pools are being dried out in an effort to exterminate harmful insects and other pests that breed in such bodies of water. This process has had beneficial results but it has also endangered the natural environment on which pond creatures depend for their lives. Those who wish to protect these helpless creatures should try to persuade authorities to use caution in draining ponds and marshes. If only one pond and its inhabitants can be saved from destruction, something of value will have been accomplished.

8 Common European Frog

As soon as the icy water begins to flow again, the common European frog, *Rana temporaria,* leaves its winter home in the mud of the pond and goes off to shallow water to find a mate. After mating has taken place, thousands of eggs are piled in mounds on the pond floor. They gradually rise up to the warmer layers of water near the surface. A frog's egg is round and enclosed in a transparent jellylike membrane; from it emerges a tadpole, which is the larval stage of the frog's development. This legless black dot with a long tail looks nothing like a frog. Only when the tadpole's legs begin to grow does its frog nature become apparent. Later on, the tail shrivels up to a stump. Then on a warm April day the little frogs leave the pond by the thousands and move out into the damp undergrowth where they gobble up small insects and snails. Many species of frogs have breeding habits similar to those of *Rana temporaria.* The adult of this species resembles the North American wood frog, *Rana sylvatica,* in appearance and in its tolerance for cold climates. Common European frogs grow up to 4 inches long.

Edible Frog

Another kind of frog found throughout Europe is the edible frog, *Rana esculenta.* This species provides most of the frogs' legs on the European market. The repetitive "querek, quack, quack" of the male edible frog is a familiar sound around a pond during the spring mating season. Each male frog usually secures a territory of its own where it sits on surface water plants, waiting for the female frogs. When one male begins to sing, a rival joins in, and soon the whole pond is full of their croaking. The chorus will stop suddenly if a frog-eating bird flies over or a man approaches. During the day the young frogs and the females often sit on the banks of the pond sunning themselves. Edible frogs eat flies, dragonflies, and other large insects which live near the water. They are so greedy that they will rush at a piece of red wool on a hook and bite hard upon it. As a result this species is easily caught. The adult edible frog measures from 2¾ to 4 inches in length, not including the creature's long legs. In the United States and Canada the bullfrog, *Rana catesbeiana,* the green frog, *Rana clamitans,* and the leopard frog, *Rana pipiens,* are the species whose legs are most often marketed for consumption.

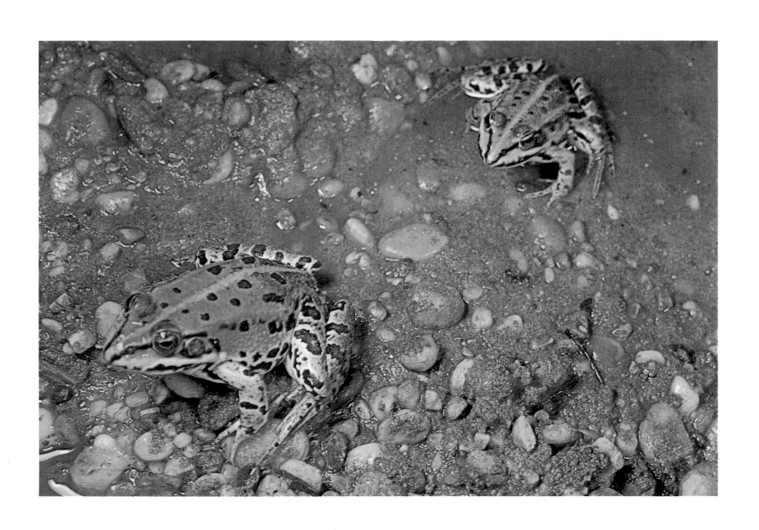

Edible Frog — Tadpole

In May the edible frog lays its eggs in large ponds and lakes. The length of time that the tadpoles develop within the eggs is influenced by the temperature of the water. The warmer the water, the faster the tadpoles will usually grow. After this period of growth the egg casing dissolves and the tiny creatures emerge. Small gills on their heads enable them to breathe under water; however, as the tadpole gets older, the external gills disappear and internal gills take their place. The tadpole now obtains oxygen from the water which passes through its mouth and into the internal gill chambers. It usually lives on algae which it scrapes off water plants with its scooplike mouth, but often hundreds of tadpoles can be seen feeding on dead fish. For a long time the tadpole remains legless and snakes its way through the algae at the bottom of the pond with the aid of its long, broad tail. Then the back legs appear, followed shortly by the front legs or arms. The tail recedes and the internal gills degenerate. The lungs begin to work and the little frog has to come to the surface to breathe. Eventually all that remains of the tail is a small stump, and the tadpole has turned into an amphibious frog.

Marsh Frog

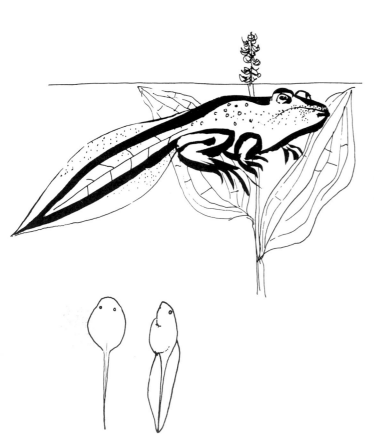

Of all the native European frogs, the marsh frog, *Rana ridibunda,* is the greediest predator. It grows so big that it can even devour the chicklets of water birds; the adult of this species sometimes measures as much as 6 inches in length. (The American bullfrog, *Rana catesbeiana,* resembles the marsh frog in size and in its predacious habits.) Because the marsh frog can make great leaps with the aid of its powerful hind legs, it is easily able to escape from danger by jumping into the pond from its resting place on the sunny bank. The frog can remain hidden under the water until the danger has passed since, like most amphibians, it has the ability to breathe through its skin as well as through its lungs. The scientific name for skin breathing is cutaneous respiration. It takes place when oxygen is absorbed directly from the water by the numerous blood vessels close to the surface of the amphibian's skin. In or out of the water, the marsh frog is an inquisitive creature. It often climbs silently up the stems of water plants to the pond's surface and, with only its nostrils and eyes above water, observes its surroundings. Marsh frogs are among the few European frogs with warts on their backs.

Jumping Frog

As its name suggests, the European jumping frog, *Rana agilis,* is noted for its ability to jump great distances. The body of the jumping frog is relatively small, up to 3¾ inches long, but its delicate, remarkably thin legs can measure over 5 inches in length. When danger threatens, this frog has been known to make leaps of over 6 feet. (The large American bullfrog is also famed as a jumper, but actually many smaller American frogs can jump farther than the bullfrog in relation to their own body lengths.) The European jumping frog has the ability to camouflage itself by changing the color of its skin to match its surroundings. When on dark soil or in water, it changes to a dark brown color; on dry, light soil it often turns a gray-white color. This species lives mainly in meadows and woods near lowland rivers, although it can sometimes be found at elevations as high as 5,000 feet. Jumping frogs spend most of their time on land and go to the river only during the spring mating season when the females lay their eggs in deep water. The small frogs, which are fully developed by June, are about ¾ inch long. Jumping frogs begin hibernation in October. The females spend the winter under leaves and in tree trunks, while the males hibernate buried in the mud.

European Green Tree Frog

When dusk has just fallen on warm June evenings, you can often hear a loud croaking in the vicinity of small ponds. The noise usually comes from bushes or reeds on the water's edge, and if the observer is lucky he can discover its source with the aid of a flashlight. The croaking sound is the mating call of the male European green tree frog, *Hyla arborea.* Clinging to a leaf or a stalk, the nocturnal singer blows up the yellow pouch under its chin until it is the size of a small balloon. This pouch or sac acts as a powerful echo chamber which amplifies the sound produced by the frog's vocal cords. The smooth skin on the back of the tree frog can turn from grass green to dull gray within two or three hours. Such color changes are related to changing weather conditions: the tree frog is usually bright green on sunny days, but when the sky becomes cloudy, its skin turns gray. The American green tree frog, *Hyla cinera,* also has the ability to change its skin color. Both the European and the American species are often considered weather forecasters because of their color-changing habits and also their tendency to sing when rainy weather is approaching. Tree frogs are generally rather small; the European green tree frog grows no bigger than 2 inches in length.

Alpine Fire-bellied Toad

Toads belonging to the genus *Bombina* — the fire-bellied toads — are found only in Europe and in Asia. The common name of the genus indicates one of its most distinctive characteristics, the brilliant yellow, red, and orange coloring on the underside of the toad's body. These colors, in sharp contrast to the dull gray of the creature's back, serve a very practical purpose. When danger threatens, the fire-bellied toad throws its head back, arches its body, and holds its arms and legs up so that the bright colors on its underside are visible. (The toad in our picture is not in the defense position; it was placed on its back so that the yellow coloring could be photographed.) This display of color confuses and discourages a hungry predator who is looking for a plain gray toad to satisfy his appetite. There are two species of fire-bellied toads in Europe. They are often called yellow-bellied and red-bellied toads, but the names "alpine fire belly" (*Bombina variegata*) and "lowland fire belly" (*Bombina bombina*) are more accurate since the most important difference between the two species is their habitat. The alpine toad of this genus lives at higher altitudes than does its close relative, the lowland fire belly. There are also differences in the toes and the skin texture of the two *Bombina* toads.

Lowland Fire-bellied Toad

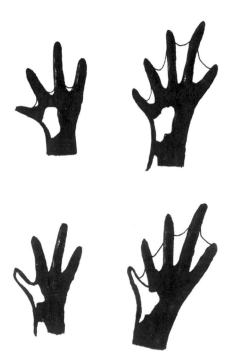

The fire-bellied toads have several characteristics which set them apart from other kinds of European and American toads. For instance, they cannot use their tongues to catch insects in the way that many other amphibians can. Fire bellies have round tongues which are fastened to the floors of their mouths, whereas the tongues of most toads and frogs are long and fastened to the front of the mouth. Another difference is habitat. The fire-bellied toads have dedicated themselves to a life in the water, in contrast to the land-dwelling habits of most other toads. They seldom leave their original pool, which can be a small water hole or even a rut in the road filled with water. They generally hang onto the edge of the pool with their legs extended and their round, wart-spotted heads and large eyes protruding above the surface. Unlucky is the insect which lands on the water in the vicinity of a fire belly: a quick leap, a loud splash, and the prey has been swallowed by this small but greedy toad. Both kinds of fire-bellied toads grow no longer than 2 inches.

24 Spadefoot Toad

In Germany the spadefoot toad is called *Knoblauchskröte* — garlic toad — because of the garlic-scented fluid it secretes when in danger. This amphibian also defends itself by rising up on its hind legs, inflating its body like a ball, and leaping at the enemy, sometimes with its mouth open. The European spadefoot, *Pelobates fuscus,* is not a true toad (all true toads are genus *Bufo*), but a frog-toad, since it bears a close resemblance to a frog. On its hind legs are sharp, horny claws for digging, and the webbing of its feet extends to the very ends of the toes. The spadefoot toad stays in the water only during mating. It spends the rest of the year in a self-made hollow and goes on hunting trips which are so regular that you can meet the same toad on the same spot at the same time day after day. The spadefoot tadpoles are the largest of all the European toads and frogs. When the young toads go out onto the land they are already about $1\frac{1}{4}$ inches long; the adult toads grow up to $3\frac{1}{8}$ inches in length. North American spadefoot toads, members of the genus *Scaphiopus,* are related to but not identical with the European spadefoots.

Midwife Toad

While all other European toads and frogs mate in water, the midwife toad, *Alytes obstetricans,* mates on land. The male wraps the strings of up to 80 large eggs around his hind legs and drags them around with him for as long as three weeks. (The male toad in our picture is carrying eggs.) Not until the eggs have developed does he take them to a pool where the tadpoles then emerge. Often tadpoles of this species develop so slowly that they have to spend the winter in the pond, and the gray baby toads do not leave the water until the following spring. The breeding habits of the midwife toad are fairly unusual in the amphibian world. All American frogs and toads abandon their eggs after laying them, but there are several other non-American species that, like the midwife toad, care for their young after mating. Midwife toads prefer to live in stony areas and are often found in old walls or under heaps of stones where they have dug themselves holes. They only emerge at nightfall to go hunting. In some areas the midwife toad is also known as the bell frog because the male can make loud calls as clear as a bell even without the aid of a vocal sac.

Common European Toad

There have been many strange legends about the common toad. In the pre-Christian era several Germanic tribes considered the toad holy. Even today some people believe that toads have "rained down from the sky" when they see hundreds of young toads suddenly emerging from a pond after a heavy rain. And everyone has heard stories — all false, of course — about the toad's wart-producing abilities. Observed from a distance, the common European toad, *Bufo bufo,* is a very ugly creature. But if you look into its shiny golden eyes and discover how quickly it becomes tame in captivity or in a garden, coming at a whistle or call and taking food from your hand, then you soon learn to think better of the common toad. It lives on worms, snails, and other garden pests and is so useful that, together with other species of toads, it has been declared a protected animal in some parts of the world. The common European toad, like the common American toad (*Bufo americanus*), spends most of the year in gardens, fields, and forests, hunting by night. It only moves to the water in spring to lay thousands of eggs in thin, jelly-covered strings which are draped over water plants and left to hatch. The adult toad grows up to 5 inches in length.

Natterjack Toad

True toads of the genus *Bufo* are found in most temperate and tropical parts of the world. There are 13 species of true toads in North America and 3 species in Europe. Of all the European toads, the natterjack, *Bufo calamita,* has become most adapted to a life on land. The webbing between its toes has almost completely disappeared. Most toads get around by hopping, in contrast to the frog's agile leaps, but because of its extremely short hind legs the natterjack toad cannot even hop. Instead it walks or runs almost like a mouse. Like all toads, the natterjack is covered with warts and has two large glands called parotoid glands located behind the eyes. When the toad is frightened or injured, these glands emit a secretion which is poisonous if swallowed. The secretion can also be very irritating to the mucous membranes of animals and humans, so anyone who handles a toad must be careful not to get the fluid in his eyes or mouth. The male natterjack toad has a large vocal sac which, when inflated to its full extent, is bigger than the creature's head. Natterjack tadpoles are very small and are fully grown when they are only 1¼ inches long. The body of an adult natterjack measures up to 2¾ inches in length.

Green Toad

The third species of European true toad is the green toad, *Bufo viridis,* which can be found in Central Europe as well as in parts of Asia. Walking in a European river valley in spring, one often hears the high trilling of the green toad's song. If the listener pursues the sound to its source, he will soon come to a pool and see the toad sitting in the water with only its head above the surface. Its trembling throat carries the sound waves into the water and the pool's surface is gently ruffled by the vibrations. At mating time the females of the species each lay 10,000 to 12,000 eggs in the water and then return to the land. During the rest of the year the green toad lives in a self-made hollow located in some warm area; it often sits at the entrance to its home, watching its surroundings attentively. More than any other species, these toads hunt by day, searching for spiders, insects, and snails. They need warmth and thus go into hibernation very early in the winter.

Palmated Newt

Very late in April another European amphibian, the palmated newt (*Triturus helveticus*), emerges from its winter quarters and looks for small streams and pools in which to breed. After the eggs are laid, the female newt fastens each one to the moss on the stream or pond bed. Ten to twenty days later the small newts emerge. That same summer they grow into adults and leave the water to find a home in damp places on land, just like their parents before them. The palmated newt lives in Western Europe, preferring areas near springs and small lakes in mountainous regions. The common name of the species is derived from its characteristic markings which resemble a hand with the fingers spread. The palmated newt is usually about 3½ inches long. It can be distinguished from the larger European pond newt (*Triturus vulgaris*) by its size and by the threadlike appendage on its tail. In addition, the male palmated newt is much less colorful and the fold of skin along its tail never develops such splendid patterns as are found on the pond newt's tail. Most species of European newts belong to the genus *Triturus*. North American newts of the genus *Diemictylus* — for instance, the red-spotted newt of the eastern United States — have habits and life cycles similar to those of the European newts.

European Pond Newt

While it is often difficult to distinguish between male and female frogs and toads, sexual dimorphism — differences in color, form, or structure between the sexes — is very obvious in newts. During the breeding period, when newts take to the water, male pond newts (*Triturus vulgaris*) develop large fluted ridges on their tails and dorsal (back) crests, and their body color intensifies enormously. The females are more plainly colored, with brown bodies and orange bellies. The female newt is pursued by the brilliantly colored male who repeatedly swims or creeps up to her, bending his trembling, outspread tail toward his body. (Because newts breathe through lungs only, their mating ceremonies must continually be interrupted in order for the couple to get their breath.) Finally the male deposits a small jelly-covered package of sperm on the floor of the pond; the female picks it up with the lips of her cloaca, a special chamber at the base of her body in which fertilization takes place. She lays the fertilized eggs on water plants and leaves them to their fate.

Larva of the Pond Newt

For a period of about two weeks, the embryo newt develops within the egg's transparent membrane. At the end of this time the small newt, or larva, is ready to leave its protective covering. It still has no hind legs but the front legs have already appeared in the form of small stumps, and enormous bundles of gills project from the larva's head. These gills extract oxygen from the water and enable the creature to breathe. Newt larvae are very greedy, living off water fleas, small water insects, and shell-fish. Soon their hind legs appear. Then as the larva grows its gills recede and lungs develop. Finally the full-grown newt leaves the water and crawls onto the land to join other older newts living under stones or in tree hollows. Moisture is necessary in the newt's habitat to prevent the amphibian's damp skin from drying out.

Crested Newt

The largest European newt is the crested or warty newt, *Triturus cristatus*. It grows to almost 7 inches long and eats water insects, worms, snails, frogs' eggs, and even young newts and salamanders. Although the crested newt is not as colorful as its smaller cousin, the pond newt, its mating habits are even more intense. During the courtship ritual, the male puts his head against the female's, as in our picture, and swirls water with his tail along the scent glands located on his lower body. These glands emit a kind of perfume which encourages the female newt to play her part in the mating activities. At the beginning of May the newt's eggs are laid on individual water plants. During the time that the embryos are developing, the adult newts also stay in the water, usually in thickly overgrown meadow ponds populated by other water creatures which provide their food. Later, after their mating colors have faded, the dark, wart-covered newts leave the pond and creep under stones and roots.

Head of the Female Crested Newt

Newts are fierce predators and the males often engage in violent struggles for food, during which they sometimes lose a leg or part of a tail. When newts are attacked by their own numerous enemies — snakes, yellow beetles, predatory beetles, and dragonfly nymphs — they must often choose between losing their lives or sacrificing a limb to the attacker. Nevertheless, one rarely sees a newt with a missing limb or healed wounds. This is because of the creature's remarkable capacity for regeneration; tails, legs, jaws, and even eyes can be rebuilt from surrounding tissue. This capability also accounts for the occasional appearance of a newt with two tails or heads, or more than four legs. If a newt embryo is damaged in the egg, then accidental regeneration sometimes takes place and two identical organs grow from the same spot.

Alpine Newt

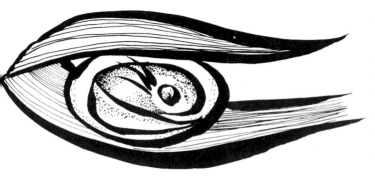

In spring the male alpine newt, *Triturus alpestris,* is a brilliant blue and orange. The female, darker and larger than the male, is also attractive because of her brilliant orange belly. The female alpine newt lays her eggs individually on the leaves of water plants; then, using her hind legs, she folds the leaf over each egg. (The American red-spotted newt lays its eggs in the same manner.) The egg's jellylike coating glues the leaf together, thus securing the developing baby against attacks from enemies. This protection is very important, for when newts lay eggs the water is still cold and the animal population of the pond is sparse. As a result there is intense competition for food. Every inhabitant of the pond grabs anything which is edible, including, of course, the freshly laid eggs of other water creatures. Alpine newts themselves are particularly greedy. You can often seen them sitting around mounds of frogs' eggs, tearing the embryos out of their coverings.

Fire Salamander

While adult newts spend at least a few months of the year in the pond, their close relatives, the European fire or spotted salamanders (*Salamandra salamandra*), stay in the water only during their larval stage. The adult of this species is strictly a land animal. Fire salamanders are somewhat larger than newts; they grow up to almost 8 inches in length, whereas the largest newts are less than 7 inches long. The fire salamander's body, particularly its head, is covered with glands which secrete a poisonous fluid. This amphibian, like the European toad, has had many legends associated with it in the past. Its common name, for instance, is derived from the ancient belief that salamanders were born out of the flames of a fire. The legend probably originated when someone saw a salamander crawling out of its hiding place in a log thrown on a bonfire. The fire salamander species is often divided into two groups, a West European breed with yellow and orange stripes and an East European group with yellow spots. Actually the creatures' color and markings seem to depend on age and the water temperature of the breeding pond rather than on geographical location. The three salamanders in our picture, although marked differently, are known to belong to the same family.

Larva of the Fire Salamander

Most species of salamanders reproduce by laying eggs, but fire salamanders bear their young alive. They mate on land, and the embryos develop in the mother's womb for about 10 months. If the weather is bad, or if the streams and pools dry up because of a drought, the female salamander can delay the birth of her young for months. When enough water is available, she enters a pond or stream and gives birth to the fully developed larvae. They are surrounded by a membrane which they immediately break with a strong blow from their tails. On the left and right sides of their heads are large bundles of external gills. During their larval period salamanders shed their skins several times. (Adult salamanders and newts also shed their skins periodically; an amphibian's skin does not stretch as the creature's body grows.) Salamander larvae grow at different rates, depending on the temperature of the water and the amount of food they get. In unfavorable conditions they can even remain in the larval stage for a whole winter.

Alpine Salamander

As their name indicates, alpine salamanders (*Salamandra atra*) live in the European Alps, sometimes at elevations over 9,000 feet. Like all amphibians, these creatures need moisture to keep their skins damp. In rainy weather one often sees hundreds of shiny black alpine salamanders creeping about on mountain paths, looking for food. They eat mostly slugs, and sometimes worms and insects. It is surprising to see this apparently slow-moving salamander shoot forward like lightning when hunting, thus catching such quick creatures as grasshoppers and other insects. Female alpine salamanders, like female fire salamanders, have adapted completely to unfavorable weather. In dry weather they can delay the birth of their young until storms have created the conditions necessary for survival. The female alpine salamander carries her young for a period of 18 months to 3 years and gives birth to two fully developed larvae.

Wood Lizard

The wood lizard or viviparous lizard, *Lacerta vivipara,* can be found throughout Europe, living in woods, moorlands, damp meadows, and mountain areas. The sex of a wood lizard can be easily distinguished by examining the creature's underside. The male's belly is yellow or orange with black legs, whereas the female has a gray or yellow belly with legs to match. On a mild July night the female wood lizard gives birth to 10 young which are fully active immediately after birth and able to go hunting for insects and small spiders. Lizards, like snakes, use their long tongues as an aid in tracking their prey. The reptiles' tongues pick up particles on the ground and transfer them to a special organ of smell located within their mouths. Wood lizards spend the winter buried deep in the ground or under stones and can be so stiff with cold that they are often taken for dead. The family to which the wood lizard belongs includes many of the common European lizards but is not native to North America. However, the racerunner lizard of the southwestern United States (genus *Cnemidophorous*) is very similar to the European wood lizard and its relatives.

The European pond turtle, *Emys orbicularis,* belongs to the large family of freshwater turtles found in many countries throughout the Northern Hemisphere. American freshwater turtles include such familiar species as the wood turtle, the diamondback terrapin, and the painted turtle. European pond turtles, like most members of the turtle family, spend many hours of the day sunning themselves on old tree stumps. However, their gray shells, often encrusted with mud, make them hard to see, and they are so shy that they immediately dive to the bottom of the water at the slightest sign of danger. Pond turtles live on fish, frogs, toads, and small water insects, and usually hunt only at night. Early in the summer the female digs a hole in the ground and lays about a dozen eggs in it. Then she fills in the hole again, carefully covering all her tracks. Pond turtles sometimes grow as large as 12 inches in length. They have a reputation for longevity and some have been known to live for more than a hundred years.

Checked Snake

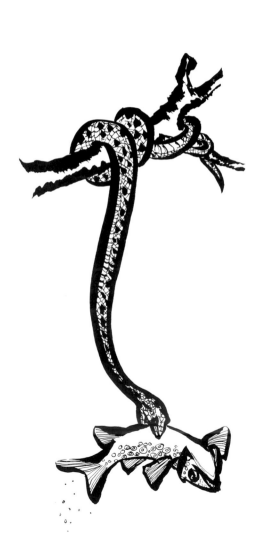

This beautiful snake is completely dependent upon water for its existence. It spends hours in the waters of its native pond or river, searching for the fish which make up its primary source of food. In fact, the checked snake leaves the aquatic environment only to hibernate and to mate. This 3½-foot-long reptile is a member of the water-snake genus, *Natrix*, species of which are found in both Europe and North America. (The European checked snake belongs to the species *Natrix tessellata*.) The female checked snake often lays her eggs in dung heaps, loose earth, or piles of leaves; in such locations the heat caused by the process of decomposition aids in the development and hatching of the eggs. Checked snakes are extraordinarily quick and shy and, as a result, are rarely seen. Snakes have no external ears but they can sense the approach of an enemy by means of ground vibrations. Thus they can escape to safety before they are noticed and disturbed. The only way to observe a snake is to catch it sleeping in the sun or to know its favorite hiding places.

Grass Snake

The European grass snake, *Natrix natrix,* is also very dependent on water. It gets its main food — newts, frogs, and small fish — from the pond or lake where it lives. This water snake is an excellent swimmer, diving continuously and even hunting while under water. On being threatened it dives out of sight immediately, but where the pond vegetation allows, it surfaces again cautiously and observes its surroundings from some leaf-covered vantage point. Even though the grass snake is not in the least poisonous, it is hunted by man and has become very shy. It has an excellent defensive weapon against all of its foes, whether human or animal: as soon as the grass snake is touched or picked up, it winds itself around the assailant and discharges large quantities of an extremely foul-smelling fluid from glands at the base of its tail. This reception effectively discourages all but the most persistent disturbers of the peace.

Head of the Grass Snake

The characteristic which all seven species of the European grass snake have in common is clearly seen in our picture — the crescent-shaped, pale yellow stripes on the side of the head. Otherwise the snakes can vary in color from gray to brown; some individual local types even have black checks on their bodies. During the summer mating season the grass snake comes very close to human habitation and often lays its eggs in farmyard dung heaps. More than two months later the 20 soft-shelled, whitish eggs hatch and the young snakes immediately start hunting for food. Even though frogs and toads are protected against enemies by poisonous skin secretions, they can still fall prey to grass snakes. The snakes, on the other hand, are also caught by amphibians. On two occasions I have seen large marsh frogs catch grass snakes behind the head and swallow them.

Common European Viper

Some of the best-known and most dangerous poisonous snakes belong to the viper family, species of which are found in both the United States and Europe. American vipers like the rattlesnake, water moccasin, and copperhead are placed in the subfamily of pit vipers, so called because of the two characteristic pits or holes on the sides of the reptiles' heads. These pits are actually complex sense organs which register temperature variations and thus enable the snake to detect the presence of warm-blooded prey. European vipers do not have facial pits; they belong to the genus *Vipera* and are called true vipers. The common European viper, *Vipera berus,* lives throughout Europe in the temperate zone. This snake, sometimes called the adder, grows up to 3 feet long and, like most other true vipers, bears its young alive. Being bitten by a viper can be a very painful and even a fatal experience. There are many conflicting opinions about the best emergency treatment to give a snake-bite victim. However, all authorities agree that the sooner the person receives professional help, the better his chances for recovery will be.

Head of the European Viper

The pointed fangs of the European viper are dangerous and effective weapons against the snake's enemies. The viper's poison or venom is stored in venom glands within its head. The venom is carried from the glands by ducts to the hollow fangs which inject the poison into the snake's prey. When not in use the deadly fangs are folded back against the roof of the mouth. They come into position only when the snake's mouth is opened wide to attack. Since such a fang can easily break off, a replacement is always in position behind it; the new fang grows quickly and soon takes on the function of the lost one. The seriousness of a viper bite can vary enormously. Depending on whether or not the snake has just made a kill, the venom glands are more or less full, thus determining the danger to a human victim. One must be careful, however, even with newly hatched vipers, which are only 6 or 7 inches in length. Even in these tiny creatures the poisoning mechanism is already fully formed and capable of functioning.

Pond Mussel

The freshwater mussel, a bivalve mollusk related to the oyster and the clam, lives in the mud and sand of pond beds as well as in the flowing waters of streams and rivers. The pond mussel grows up to almost 8 inches in length. Its protective shell, thin and yellowish in color, is lined with an iridescent material called mother-of-pearl, which is often used to make pearl buttons. Between the two pieces or valves of the pond mussel's shell lies the creature's sensitive body. When danger threatens, strong muscles on the shell's hinge close its two halves, and the mussel is safe from most of its enemies. Bivalves like the mussel breathe by means of gills which extract oxygen from the water taken into the shell cavity. This intake of water also provides the creature's food. A screen of hair-like projections on the gills filters out impurities in the water at the same time that it allows microscopic organisms called infusoria to enter the mussel's digestive system. Mussels move by means of a fleshy foot which is extended from the shell and used to pull the creature along the bed of the pond. The pond mussel in our picture belongs to the European species *Anodonta cygnea;* many North American fresh water mussels are also members of the genus *Anodonta.*

Greater Pond Snail and Ramshorn Snail

These two species of freshwater snails are most common in thickly overgrown ponds. Since they belong to the order of snails that have lungs rather than gills, they have to come to the surface of the water in order to breathe. Each of the snails has a pair of feelers or tentacles on the ends of which are its eyes. Both species live mainly off vegetable matter, but they also eat dead animals, thus serving as scavengers in the pond community. The greater pond snail (left) has a spiral shell about 2⅜ inches long, usually twisted to the right and ending in a point. The ramshorn snail's shell is coiled to the left and is flat, like a plate. In order to increase the size of their portable houses, snails extract calcium from their diets and build onto the opening of the shell. The snail's digestive organs are safely enclosed inside this protective covering; the muscular foot and the head can be withdrawn into the shell as well if danger threatens. The greater pond snail, *Lymnaea stagnalis,* is native to both North America and Europe. The ramshorn snail, *Planorbis corneus,* belongs to a European species with close relatives in the United States.

70 Common Freshwater Sponge

Many people are surprised to learn that sponges are not plants but animals or colonies of animals. It is still more surprising to discover that sponges can be found in freshwater rivers and ponds as well as in warm ocean waters. Some freshwater sponges look like forked tree branches, but most often they take the form of a slimy coating on the stalks of water plants. (The freshwater sponges in our picture belong to the genus *Spongilla,* which is common in both Europe and North America.) The body of this kind of sponge consists of two layers of cells enclosing a central cavity. Between the two layers is a jellylike material containing free-moving cells which aid in digestion, elimination of wastes, and building of the sponge's skeleton. Water enters the sponge by means of tiny holes or pores which connect with channels leading to the cavity. The water is moved through the sponge by special cells on the cavity wall; each of these cells has a long, threadlike appendage called a flagellum, which whips through the water and creates a current. After the cells extract oxygen and food materials from the water, it is expelled through a large opening at the top of the sponge.

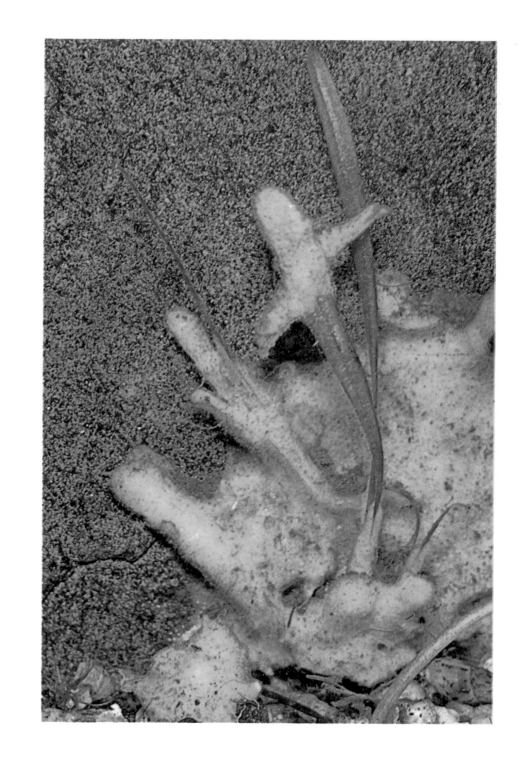

Brown Freshwater Hydra

When we bring water plants home with us from the pond and search them for living creatures, we do not often see the tiny animals called hydras which are usually attached to the plants' leaves and stalks. These strange little creatures have a habit of curling up into balls when they are disturbed. When they are uncurled, their thin, transparent bodies extend to about ½ inch in length. The long tentacles attached to one end of the hydra's body can measure as much as 10 inches when fully extended. The freshwater hydra is closely related to the jellyfish and the sea anemone and has one of the simplest structures of all the many-celled animals in existence. Hydras have no heads and only one opening at the top of the body through which food is taken in and wastes eliminated. The creatures remain attached to rocks or water plants and catch food with their tentacles, which float around them in the water. These tentacles shoot out long, poisonous threads which penetrate the prey's body and paralyze it. Then the tentacles pull the victim into the hydra's body where it is digested in the central cavity. Freshwater hydras come in several different colors; the brown hydra belongs to the genus *Pelmatohydra*.

Four-spotted Dragonfly

Dragonflies are familiar insects found near ponds and streams in many parts of the world. The four-spotted dragonfly, *Libellula quadri-maculata,* lives near European waters but has many close relatives in North America. This insect likes to sit on the tops of dry branches or in the reeds, observing its surroundings intently. If a fly approaches, the dragonfly hastily takes to the air, catches the prey with its legs, and devours it in flight with its sharp, daggerlike teeth. Because the dragonfly's wings consist of a network of veins and, as a result, are enormously stable, the insect is a real master of the air. Dragonflies have been known to fly more than 60 miles an hour over a short distance; they can also hover in one spot, remaining almost motionless. With their individually controlled wings they can even fly backwards. After mating in the air the female dragonfly hovers over shallow lakes and ponds and then rushes down to lay her eggs under the surface of the water. The eggs hatch in 5 to 15 days and the young dragonflies emerge to begin their larval development in the pond.

Head of the Four-spotted Dragonfly

Insects' eyes are completely different from the eyes of all vertebrates. In our picture we can see that the two large eyes which curve around the dragonfly's head consist of thousands of individual lenses or facets. Each tiny lens picks up a slightly different portion of the insect's visual field and transfers the image to the brain. Here all the images are combined in a kind of composite picture of the dragonfly's surroundings. Thus, by means of this compound eye the insect can survey all of its environment at one time. Each movement in front of it, behind it, or to one side can be registered, whether it be the swaying of grass in the wind, a buzzing fly tempting the dragonfly to a hunting trip, or the approach of an enemy, necessitating rapid flight. This efficient warning system is very useful since dragonflies have many enemies among birds and other vertebrates. It is not easy for a human observer to get close to a dragonfly. Only when you approach it very slowly and keep within the safety margin can you observe this insect at close quarters.

Larva of the Four-spotted Dragonfly

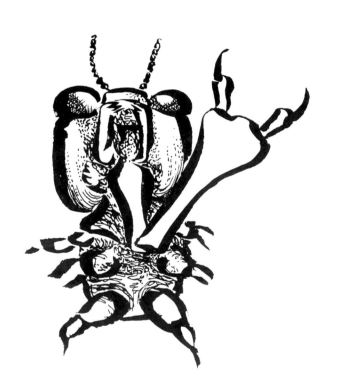

On the beds of streams and on the stems of water plants, in any season, you will find strange insects which bear no resemblance to the winged dragonfly. Yet these creatures, called nymphs, are the dragonfly's larval form. They have adapted themselves completely to life underwater, having in their hind quarters an internal gill system into which they suck oxygen-rich water. The nymph of the four-spotted dragonfly has hairs over all of its upper surface, which collect bits of plants and mud. Thus camouflaged, it sits almost motionless on the stream bed, waiting for prey; dragonfly nymphs, like their parents, are predatory creatures. At the front of their heads they have a traplike lip, which looks something like the shovel of an excavator. If a water flea, crayfish, tadpole, fish, or even a smaller dragonfly approaches, the nymph shoots its lip forward, seizes the prey, and pulls it back into its mouth. When it is not in use, this unusual organ is folded back over the creature's face like a kind of mask.

Damselfly

Dragonflies and their close relatives, the damselflies, make up an ancient order of insects called Odonata. In prehistoric times there were thousands of species of these insects, some of which were much larger than their modern descendents. Scientists have discovered fossils of primitive dragonflies with wingspans of more than 2 feet. Modern dragonflies have wingspans averaging no more than 3 or 4 inches, and damselflies are usually about half this size. These delicate creatures move more slowly than their larger cousins of the dragonfly family. They can often be seen fluttering daintily around a pond or stream or sitting on reed stems and rushes. Nevertheless, they can move quickly when necessary, for damselflies, like dragonflies, live by preying on other insects. In mating, the male and female damselflies form a heart-shaped arch. Then, still joined, they fly to the rush beds on the stream's edge and the female deposits her eggs in the juicy core of a rush stalk. (In our picture, damselflies of the species *Lestes sponsa* are laying their eggs.) In some species the female goes under the water and attaches her eggs to the stem near the plant's roots.

Head of the Damselfly

Both members of the order Odonata have many characteristics in common, but they differ in some ways. As we can see in our picture, the head of the damselfly looks quite different from the head of the four-spotted dragonfly. The damselfly's compound eyes are smaller and they form two widely separated spheres, one on each side of the head, instead of covering the insect's whole head. In addition to their compound eyes, both damselflies and dragonflies have three small light-sensitive organs called simple eyes located in the center of the head. Like the dragonfly, the damselfly can control each of its four wings individually, but it usually moves them in pairs. When the front wings move forward, the back wings move backward, thus producing a completely regular flight. The insect alternates its periods of flight with long rest periods during which it glides with its wings outspread and motionless. Most Odonata have colored bodies and transparent wings, but some species of damselflies belonging to the genus *Agrion* have beautiful iridescent wings of blue and green. The wings of *Agrion maculatum,* a damselfly native to the United States, are iridescent black and its body a shining metallic green.

Larva of the Damselfly

Damselflies and dragonflies differ somewhat in their larval forms as well as in the adult stage. For instance, the damselfly nymph breathes through external gills, which appear in our picture as leaflike appendages at the end of the abdomen. The dragonfly nymph has an internal respiration system. What the two Odonata insects do have in common, however, is a kind of development called incomplete metamorphosis. They do not go through the four stages of development — egg, larva, pupa, and adult — which make up the life cycles of insects like butterflies and moths. The pupa stage is missing in the metamorphosis of damselflies and dragonflies. After the Odonata larva or nymph hatches, it remains in the water for one to five years; during this period of development it sheds its skin about 12 times. Finally the nymph is ready to leave the water. It creeps up the stem of a reed and clings there motionless for several hours. Then its skin begins to split along the back. The opening gradually widens and the adult insect emerges, its wings still soft and folded together. Metamorphosis takes place so quickly after the nymph leaves the pond that it will drown if it falls back into the water. This is because the insect's water-breathing respiration system has already been replaced by an air-breathing one.

Water Strider

The ability to walk on water seems so remarkable that man often considers it a sign of miraculous power. In the insect world, however, there are several creatures which possess this peculiar ability. The most accomplished of the group is the water strider, an insect belonging to the order Hemiptera — the true bugs. The water strider's long legs are widely spread and its foot segments have oil glands that make them water-resistant. These characteristics enable the insect to glide or walk on the surface film of the water just as humans walk on ice. However, if you put liquid soap into the pond or try to keep a captive water strider in a water-filled container which was once washed with soap, then the insect is in trouble. Its legs sink and it drowns ingloriously. A water strider usually measures about 1 1/8 inches in length. It feeds off other insects which have been blown onto the surface of the water, seizing them with its clawlike front legs. Like all Hemiptera, water striders have sharp mouths or beaks which enable them to pierce the bodies of their prey and suck out fluids. The most common American and European water striders belong to the genus *Gerris;* the insect in our picture is a member of the species *Gerris lacustris.*

Water Scorpion

The water bug called the water scorpion was named because of its slight resemblance to the real, land-dwelling scorpion. Both creatures have long, narrow tails; however, the land scorpion uses its tail for stinging, while the water scorpion's tail is actually a breathing tube. The insect sticks this tube above the surface of the water and breathes through it in the same way that a diver breathes through a snorkel. The water scorpion, like other water bugs, is a fierce predator. It catches insects, tadpoles, and small fish with its clawlike front legs and sucks the prey's blood through a pointed, tubular beak. In summer the water scorpion spends its time on the beds of stagnant or slow-moving streams where it creeps cautiously around in search of prey. Members of the water scorpion family differ a great deal in appearance. Insects of the genus *Ranatra,* like the one in our picture, have thin, cylindrical bodies about 2¾ inches long and are sometimes called water needles. Water scorpions belonging to the genus *Nepa* are broad and flat. Both have the long breathing tube which is characteristic of the water scorpion family.

Backswimmer

The fact that water insects are able to adjust their specific weight to the weight of the water by taking in air gives these creatures considerable freedom of choice as far as body position and direction of motion are concerned. The water bug called the backswimmer takes advantage of this freedom by choosing to spend most of its time swimming or floating on its back. The backswimmer has a boat-shaped body, about 5/8 inch in length, and long, hairy hind legs which it uses like oars when swimming. In hunting, the insect often drifts up under its prey, seizes the victim with its front legs, and kills it by injecting poison with its sharp beak. The backswimmer's bite is not fatal to humans as it is to small water creatures, but it can be very painful. Care must be used in capturing this water bug, and some of its relatives as well: the water scorpion, for instance, can also inflict a painful skin puncture. The backswimmer in our picture belongs to the genus *Notonecta;* various species of this genus are found in ponds and streams throughout the world.

Common Mosquito

Freshwater ponds and marshes often serve as breeding places for a familiar insect pest, the common mosquito (*Culex pipiens*). This insect is notorious for its irritating bite. Actually, it is only the female mosquito that is responsible for such attacks, which are not really "bites" at all, but skin punctures. The insect pierces the skin of its victim, either human or animal, with its needlelike mouth parts and sucks out blood through the puncture. (Females of some species need blood in order to lay eggs.) The mosquito's saliva causes the itchy welt that we call a mosquito bite. Since some species of mosquitoes are disease-carriers as well as pests, many efforts have been made to reduce their numbers. Unfortunately, chemical attacks on mosquitoes and their breeding ponds have destroyed other more useful members of the insect world. Today methods have been developed to control the mosquito population without harming other insects. The flight noises of female mosquitoes are broadcast over loudspeakers to attract the males, who are caught, sterilized, and set free again. Females who mate with the sterilized males produce eggs which will not develop.

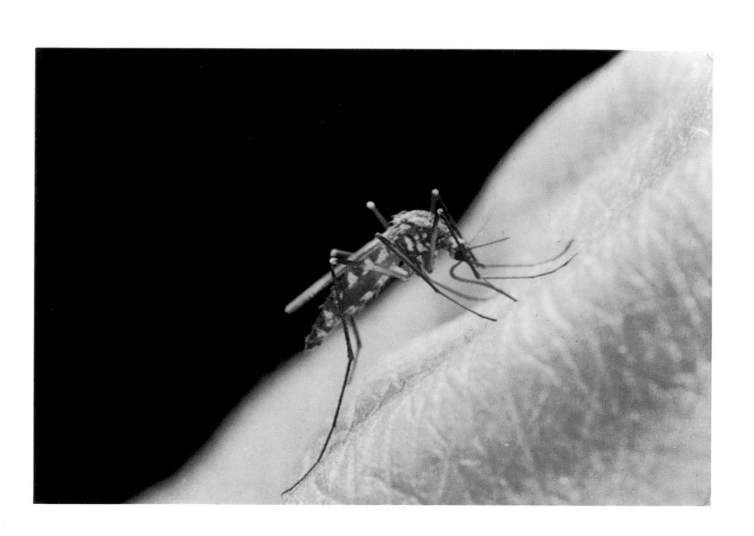

Larva of the Caddisfly

The larva of the insect called the caddisfly is a master of camouflage and self-protection. The caddisfly is the only member of the order Trichoptera, and the adult insect closely resembles the butterfly and the moth, except that it has hairs on its wings instead of scales. In their larval stage caddisflies live on the beds of streams and ponds in protective cases which they have constructed from surrounding materials. They use many different kinds of building materials for their underwater houses, and each species usually has its own special style of architecture. Some larvae build their cases out of grains of sand fastened onto a silklike substance produced by body glands. Others use small snail shells, often with the living snails still inside them, or make cone-shaped structures out of leaves. The species pictured here, *Limnephilus rhombicus,* uses small twigs for its artistic but practical home. Caddisflies are found in almost all parts of the world and in almost all kinds of aquatic environments, from the icy, fast-flowing mountain stream to the quiet meadow pond. The cases constructed by larvae living in swift-moving water tend to be heavier, and thus less subject to the water current, than the cases of the pond-dwelling caddisflies.

Diving Water Beetle, genus *Dytiscus*

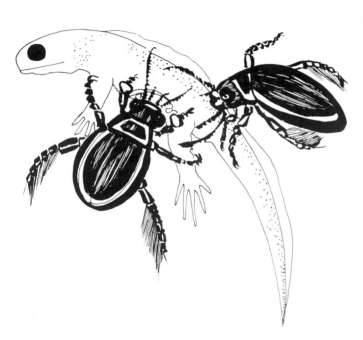

The most dangerous enemy of all small water creatures is the 1½-inch-long diving water beetle of the genus *Dytiscus,* which is found in all parts of the world. This hungry predator even attacks some of the larger fish. Its powerful hind legs are fringed with long hairs and are flattened to such an extent that they resemble flippers. With the aid of these efficient oars, the diving beetle swims rapidly through lakes and ponds in search of prey. It prefers tadpoles, newts, and fish but it does not hesitate to attack fellow beetles when nothing else is available. The prey is grasped with the front legs and eaten alive. Diving beetles, like other aquatic insects, must rise to the surface of the pond in order to breathe. In their adult stage, most insects obtain oxygen through small openings in their bodies called spiracles which connect with an internal system of air tubes. When it needs oxygen, the diving beetle comes to the surface, raises the back part of its body above water, and fills its respiratory system with air. At the same time it traps air bubbles beneath its wings. By making use of this dual air supply, the beetle can spend quite a long time under water.

Diving Water Beetle, genus *Acilius*

Diving water beetles of the European genus *Acilius* are about half the size of their cousins, the *Dytiscus* beetles, and are therefore less likely to prey on fish. Instead these beetles concentrate on a diet of snails and insect larvae. Male beetles of this genus have claws on their front legs, and their wing surfaces are smooth and brown with yellowish dots. The wing surfaces of the females are furrowed and covered with long hairs. These lively little beetles usually live in stagnant water; they make their homes in small ponds or even puddles overgrown with algae. Like the larger diving beetles, they must come to the water surface from time to time in order to fill their air-tube systems and the spaces under their wings with air. Then they dive again and continue their endless search for food. While under water, the diving beetle expels used air in the form of bubbles.

Larva of the *Acilius* Diving Beetle

In the depths of the pond or pool, where rotting leaves and branches collect, one almost always finds predatory water creatures lying in wait for prey. If the collector scoops out a pile of pond debris in a net and examines it leaf by leaf, he will usually discover some interesting specimens of underwater life. The larva of the *Acilius* diving beetle, for instance, often makes its home in such an environment. This rather unpleasant-looking creature is sometimes called a water tiger, and for good reason. If you put an *Acilius* larva into an aquarium with other creatures, it will soon grow fat and the population of the aquarium will rapidly decrease. One quick grab of the water tiger's sharp jaws and the prey is caught. The larva then pumps its digestive juices into the victim. Digestion takes place externally, within the prey's own body; the water tiger sucks out the resulting fluids and leaves the undigested portions of the body behind.

Freshwater Crayfish

The freshwater crayfish, a crustacean closely related to the lobster and the crab, lives in the rivers and lakes of every continent except Africa. The crayfish's tough shell, made of a substance called chitin (*kite* un), protects the creature's body so well that it does not need an internal skeleton. This coat of armor contains a large amount of lime and is so hard that it cannot increase in size as its owner grows. The crayfish must shed its shell several times before it reaches its maximum length, usually about 5½ inches. Crayfish, like some other members of the crustacean family, have unique organs of balance which tell them if they are upright in the water. These organs, located at the base of the one of the creature's antennae, are small water-filled sacs with grains of sand in them. On the floors of the sacs are fine hairs which are very sensitive to touch. When the crustacean is in an upright position, the force of gravity presses the sand grains against these hairs, which send a signal to the creature's brain. European crayfish, like the one in our picture, belong to the genus *Astacus*. The North American crayfish is genus *Cambarus*.

Freshwater Shrimp

You can often find these peculiar freshwater crustaceans hiding under stones in rivers and streams. They usually try to escape by contracting their powerful abdominal muscles and shooting backward through the water, but they are easily caught, even by hand. The body of the freshwater shrimp, about ¾ inch in length, is flat and almost transparent. The female shrimp has a breeding sac on her front legs in which her eggs develop and hatch. Freshwater shrimp are most active at night when they roam the waters, eating the remains of rotting plants and dead animals. They play an important role in the underwater community by getting rid of this decaying matter and also by providing an abundant source of food for fish. Freshwater shrimp need a lot of oxygen in their environment. When streams become polluted, these useful little creatures cannot survive. The freshwater shrimp in our picture belongs to the genus *Gammarus,* which is found in both Europe and North America.

Water Flea

Despite its name, the water flea is not an insect but a tiny crustacean, distantly related to the crayfish and the shrimp. Scientists usually prefer to call the water flea daphnia since it makes up a genus of that name. The creature was probably given its common name because of its size and its characteristic skipping and jumping movements. The water flea's minute body, about $1/10$ inch long, is surrounded by a transparent shell through which the action of the creature's heart and other organs can be observed. Water fleas feed on infusoria and algae in the water and are themselves the most important food for many larger water creatures. These little crustaceans have rather unusual reproductive habits. They reproduce themselves primarily by parthenogenesis, a form of reproduction in which new life develops from unfertilized eggs. The eggs hatch within the breeding sac under the female water flea's shell. During some seasons, however, water fleas produce eggs which must be fertilized in order to develop. The fertilized eggs are dropped into the water in autumn and do not hatch until the following spring. Numerous species of water fleas are found in freshwater ponds and lakes throughout the world; all belong to the genus *Daphnia*.

Books in This Series

AMONG THE PLAINS INDIANS

BIRDS OF THE WORLD
in Field and Garden

CREATURES OF POND AND POOL

AQUARIUM FISH
from Around the World

WILD ANIMALS OF AFRICA

These fact-filled books contain more than fifty four-color plates and over 100 pages. Printed on high quality paper and reinforced bound, these books will add an exciting new dimension to any collection.

AMONG THE PLAINS INDIANS, a fictional account based on the actual travels of two explorers who observed American Indian life in the 1830's, features illustrations by artists George Catlin and Karl Bodmer.

BIRDS OF THE WORLD in Field and Garden combines colorful photographs and an informative text to describe some of the world's most interesting birds.

CREATURES OF POND AND POOL describes many of the beautiful and unusual creatures — frogs, water snakes, salamanders, aquatic insects — that live in and around fresh-water ponds.

AQUARIUM FISH from Around the World presents an exciting picture of the varied species of fish that inhabit the miniature world of an aquarium.

WILD ANIMALS OF AFRICA takes the reader on a safari with German naturalist Klaus Paysan, who tells of his adventures in Africa and describes the living habits of the continent's most fascinating animals.

For more information about these and other quality books for young people, please write to

LERNER PUBLICATIONS COMPANY

241 First Avenue North, Minneapolis, Minnesota 55401